Bedtime Tales

Unit 2 Reader

Skills Strand
GRADE 2

Amplify learning.

Core Knowledge®

ISBN 978-1-61700-208-3

Printed in the USA
NA05 LSCOW 2017

Table of Contents
Bedtime Tales
Unit 2 Reader

Mike's Bedtime

Mike had his jet plane in his left hand.

"Zip! Zing!" he yelled. "Take that, T. Rex!"

Just then, his dad came in and said, "Mike, it's bedtime."

"But, Dad," Mike said, "I'm seven! Can't I sit up a bit?"

Mike's dad said, "Not if the sun is down and the street lamp is on. Then, it's bedtime."

Mike said, "But, if the street lamp is off, it's not bedtime yet!"

Mike ran to check on the lamp and the sun. He yanked back the drapes. The sun had set. It was pitch black. The street lamp was glinting in the blackness. It was bedtime.

"Ug!" Mike said. He slumped and let his chin drop on his chest.

"Bedtime!" said his dad.

Mike limped to his bed and plopped down on it. He made a face that said, "I wish it was not bedtime!"

Mike's dad smiled. "What if I tell you a bedtime tale?" he asked. "Would that help?"

Mike did not think it would help much. He shrugged.

"When I was a kid," his dad said, "your Gramp would tell me bedtime tales. I liked them. I'll bet I can still tell a lot of them."

"OK," said Mike, "I would like one bedtime tale." Mike's dad sat down on the bed and patted Mike on the back of the neck. "This is a bedtime tale your Gramp liked to tell me," he said.

The Milk

Mike's dad was getting set to tell a bedtime tale. H
said, "The name of this bedtime tale is *The Milk*."

Once upon a time, a lass named Jane set off from home to sell a bucket of milk.

As she went, she was thinking of the cash she would get from selling the milk.

"I have big plans. I will sell this milk," she said, "and I will use the cash to get a hen. I hope my hen will make lots of eggs."

"Then I will sell those eggs and use the cash to get a cute piglet. I will take care of the piglet and let him munch on pig slop till he gets nice and plump."

"Then I will sell the pig and get a nice dress that I can dance in, and . . ."

But just as she was thinking of the dress, she tripped on a stone and the bucket fell with a crash. The milk splashed on the path. Jane made a face and fumed at the spilt milk.

Moral: Take one step at a time.

"Is that the end?" asked Mike.

"That's it," said his dad.

"What a shame!" said Mike. "She had such big plans!"

Mike's dad nodded. "You can make plans, but planning by itself will not make things happen."

Mike sat thinking a bit. Then he said, "Dad, that bedtime tale was not bad. But it was sad. Next time would you tell a fun tale?"

"Yes," said his dad. "Next time."

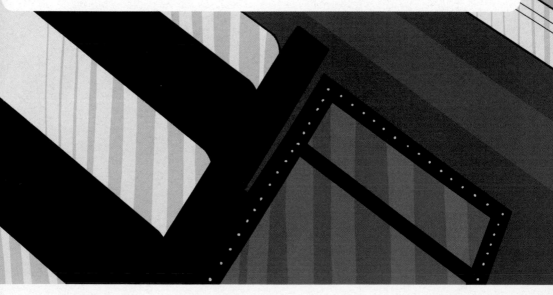

The Jumping Frog

"Dad," Mike said, "you said we could have a fun bedtime tale this time. Have you got one that's fun?"

"Yes," said his dad. "I've got one I think you will like. It's a tale my dad used to like to tell. It takes place in the West a long time back in the past. The name of the tale is *The Jumping Frog*."

Once there was a man named Big Jim who had a frog.

Big Jim held the frog up and made a speech. "This here is the best jumping frog in the land!" he said. "This frog has speed. It can jump three feet at once. You think your frog can jump? I'll bet he can't jump like my frog! In fact, I got ten bucks says there's not a frog in the land can jump as fast as this frog. This frog hops like the wind. This frog . . ."

Well, Big Jim would have kept on bragging, but, just then, a man in a black vest got up and spoke.

"My name is Pete. I'm not from here," said the man. "And I do not have a frog. But if I did, I would take the bet and race your frog."

"Well, shucks," said Big Jim. "That's not a problem. Here, take my frog. I'll run down to the stream and catch you a frog so we each have a frog to compete in the race." Big Jim handed his frog to Pete. Then he ran off to the stream.

21

Mike's dad was not finished telling the tale, but Mike had drifted off to sleep. He gave Mike a kiss and hoped he would have sweet dreams.

The Frog Race

"Dad," Mike said when he woke up, "what happened with the jumping frog? I missed the end of the tale. I was sleeping."

"I did not tell it to the end," said his dad. "When you drifted off to sleep, I stopped."

"Oh, tell the ending!" said Mike.

Mike's dad picked up the tale where he had left off.

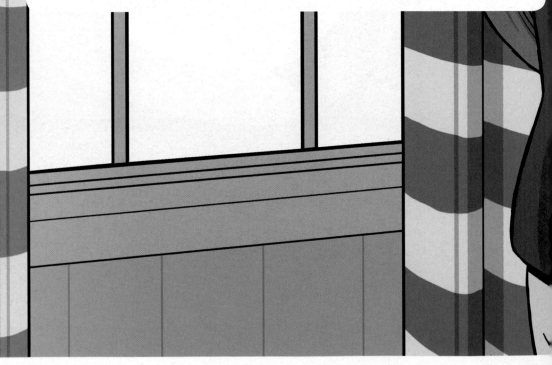

Big Jim handed his frog to Pete and ran off to the stream.

Pete held Big Jim's frog in his hand. Pete looked at the frog. Then Pete reached into his pocket and got a pile of limes. Yum—Big Jim's frog drooled. The frog ate the whole pile of limes from Pete's hand! Then Pete set the frog down.

While Pete was feeding the frog limes, Big Jim was down at the stream. He tossed off his boots and went frog hunting. At last he nabbed a nice green frog. He ran back and handed the frog to Pete.

"There's your frog!" said Jim. "Just set him down there next to my frog. Then we will let them compete to see which one of them is the fastest!"

Pete set his frog down.

"All set?" said Jim.

"All set," said the man.

Then Jim yelled, "Jump, frogs, jump!"

Pete gave the two frogs a tap to get them jumping. His frog hopped off nice and quick. But Jim's frog just sat there. Once he hitched up his legs like he was fixing to jump. But it was no use. With all those limes in him, he was planted there just as solid as a rock. His tummy was full!

Pete's frog hopped and hopped till it got to the finish line.

"Fine race!" said Pete. He took Jim's ten bucks and slipped the cash in his pocket. Then Pete tipped his hat and set off.

Well, Big Jim was stunned. "What happened to my frog?" he said. "I hope he's not sick."

He bent down and picked up the frog and rubbed his tummy.

"Goodness!" said Jim. "He must have had a big lunch!"

"I think Pete tricked me! He fed my frog too much to eat!" Jim said. Big Jim let out a whoop. His face got red. Jim ran to catch Pete. But it was no use. Pete had run off. Pete had tricked Big Jim!

The Hare and the Hedgehog

Mike and his dad sat on the bed.

"Did you like the tale of *The Jumping Frog?*" Mike's dad asked.

"Yes," said Mike. "I liked how Pete tricked Jim by feeding his frog the limes!"

"Then I think you will like this next tale as well. It involves a trick, too. The name of this one is *The Hare and the Hedgehog.*"

"What's a hare?"

"It's like a rabbit."

"OK. Tell it!"

35

Once there was a hare who was proud of his speed. He liked to brag. "I'm so fast!" he said. "I am the fastest! No one is as fast as me!"

Well, the hedgehog got sick of all this bragging. He set himself to thinking how he could trick the hare and get him to stop bragging all the time.

The hedgehog made a plan. He went to the hare and said, "Let's race!"

The hare smiled. "You and I?" he said. "Is this a joke? What would be the point? Those legs of yours are like stumps. It must take you from sunrise until sundown to hike a mile!"

"Will you join me in a race?" said the hedgehog.

"I will join you!" said the hare.

"Good," said the hedgehog. "We will race south from this fence up to the house on the hill. But I can't race till I have my lunch. I'll be back at one."

Then the hedgehog went home and spoke to his wife.

"Wife," he said, "at one I will run a race with the hare."

"What?" said his wife. She frowned and asked, "Are you out of your wits? He's so fast! You can't hope to win a race with him."

"Trust me," said the hedgehog. "I have a plan."

"What's his plan?" asked Mike.

"I will tell you next time," said his dad.

"Well, rats!" said Mike. "It was just getting good! I wish you could just tell me now."

"Next time," said his dad.

How the Hedgehog Tricked the Har

"Where was it I left off?" asked Mike's dad.

"The hedgehog was telling his wife the plan to trick the hare," said Mike.

"Got it!" said his dad.

The hedgehog made a map of his plan. He pointed to the map and outlined his plan to trick the hare.

"The hare and I will race from down by the fence up to the house on the hill," the hedgehog said to his wife. "I need you to stand next to the house. Stand in a spot where the hare can't see you. And be on the lookout, my dear!"

The hedgehog's wife nodded and said, "Your map is clear. I will be there."

The hedgehog went on, "When the hare gets close, you must pop out and shout, 'There you are! What took you so long?' But when you do this, make your voice deep and stern like my voice. The hare can't tell one hedgehog from the next. If you sound like me, he will think you are me. And he will think that he has lost the race!"

"What a clever plan!" said his wife. "It's perfect!"

46

She puckered up and kissed him on one of his cheeks, where he had no spikes. The hedgehog handed his wife the map.

After his meal, the hedgehog went to the fence. His wife went up to the house on the hill.

The hedgehog and the hare lined up.

"All set?" said the hare.

"All set," said the hedgehog.

"Run!" said the hare.

The hare bounded off. He was a fast and powerful runner. In a flash he ran down the hill, past the well, and up to the house.

When he got to the top of the hill, there was a hedgehog standing next to the house.

It was the hedgehog's wife, but she spoke in a deep, stern voice like a male hedgehog. "There you are!" she said. "What took you so long?"

The hare was stunned. "It can't be!" he said. "How did you get here so fast? I will race you back to the fence!"

And so the hare ran back past the well and up the hill until he got back to the fence.

And what did he see when he got there?

A hedgehog! This time it was the male hedgehog. The hedgehog said, "There you are! What took you so long?"

"No, no, no!" screamed the hare. The hare lost his temper. "It can't be. It can't be. I am faster. I will race you back to the house! You can't beat me!"

So the hare ran back up the hill, past the well, and up to the house.

And what did he see when he got there?

A hedgehog! This time it was the hedgehog's wife. In a deep, stern voice, she said, "There you are! What took you so long?"

The hare ran to the fence and back ten times. But it was the same all ten times. At last he was so tired out that he fell on the ground next to the male hedgehog. He could not stop huffing and puffing. He frowned and said, with a gasp, "I feel weak. You are faster and better than me!"

The hedgehog just smiled.

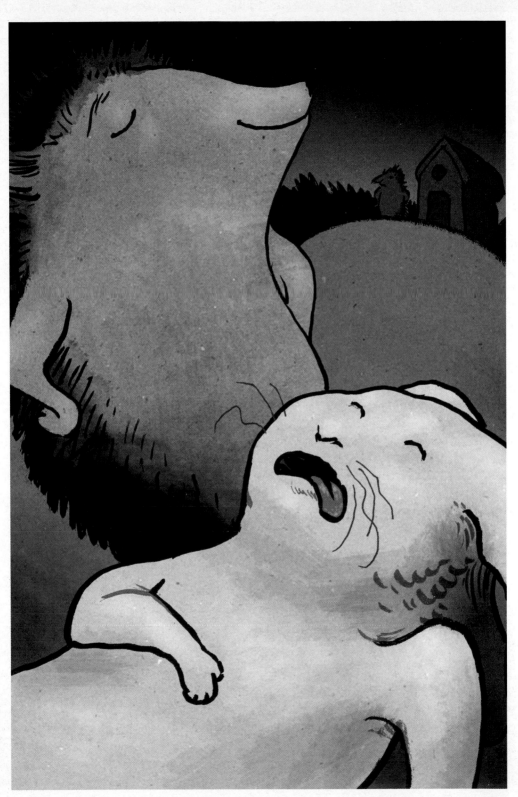

The Pancake, Part I

"Did you enjoy the tale of the hedgehog and the hare?"
asked Mike's dad.

"Yes, I liked it," said Mike. "The hedgehog came up
with a good trick."

"The tale I'd like to tell you next has a trick in it, too."

"Cool!" said Mike. "Is there a hedgehog in it?"

"Nope," said his dad. "But there is a pancake in it!"

"A pancake?"

"Yep."

"Neat! Tell it!"

"But the sun has not set yet! The street lamp is not on yet!"

"Please! I would like to hear it! Will you tell the pancake tale!"

Once upon a time there was a mom who had six kids. One morning the mom was grilling a pancake for the kids. The kids looked at the pancake. They got out their forks and started licking their lips.

The pancake looked back at the kids. He was scared. He feared the kids would eat him. When the mom was not looking, the pancake jumped out of the pan and ran off.

The pancake ran out of the house.

"Stop, pancake!" shouted the mom from the porch.

"Stop, pancake!" shouted the six kids.

All seven of them chased the pancake as he ran out of the yard.

But the pancake was too fast. He outran them all.

The pancake ran north on a foot path. He zoomed past a barn and two farmers who were plowing the ground.

"Why are you running, pancake?" the farmers asked.

The pancake shouted, "I've outrun a mom and six kids, and I can outrun you too! I'm too fast and too smart for you."

"You think so?" said the farmers. They started running. But the pancake was too fast. He outran the farmers.

61

Just then Mike's sister Ann came in. She was just three. She had on her gown for bed.

"Dad," she said, "will you tell it to me, too?"

"Yes, I will," said her dad. "You can sit up here with Mike and hear the rest of the tale."

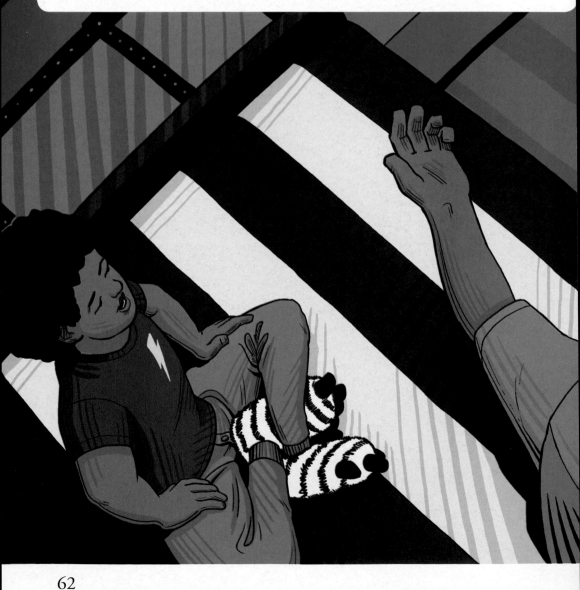

The Pancake, Part II

"Let's see," said Mike's dad. "Where did I stop?"

"The pancake was running," said Mike. "He had just outrun the two farmers."

"OK," said Mike's dad. "Let's start there."

The pancake ran on until, by and by, he ran past a pig.

"Why are you running, pancake?" the pig asked.

The pancake shouted, "I've outrun a mom, six kids, and two farmers, and I can outrun you too! I am too fast and too smart for you."

"You think so?" said the pig. Then it snorted and started running. The pig chased the pancake. But the pancake was too fast.

The pancake ran on until, by and by, he ran past a hen.

"Why are you running, pancake?" the hen asked.

The pancake shouted, "I've outrun a mom, six kids, two farmers, and a pig, and I can outrun you too! I am too fast and too smart for you."

"You think so?" said the hen. Then she set off, clucking as she ran. The hen chased the pancake. But the pancake was too fast.

The pancake went on until, by and by, he ran past a fox.

"Why are you running, pancake?" the fox asked.

The pancake said, "I've outrun a mom, six kids, two farmers, a pig, and a hen, and I can outrun you too! I am too fast and too smart for you!"

The fox did not get up. He just sat there and said, "What was that you said? I could not quite make it out."

The pancake stopped running and yelled, **"I've outrun a mom, six kids, two farmers, a pig, and a hen, and I can outrun you too! I am too fast and too smart for you!"**

The fox squinted and said, "What was that you said? I still could not quite hear you. Why do you stand so far off? Stand nearer to me so I can hear you."

The pancake ran up near to the fox. Then he shouted at the top of his lungs: **"I'VE OUTRUN A MOM, SIX KIDS, TWO FARMERS, A PIG, AND A HEN, AND I CAN OUTRUN YOU TOO! I AM TOO FAST AND TOO SMART FOR YOU!"**

"You think so?" said the fox. "I think you made a mistake and got a bit too close." Then he scooped the pancake into his mouth and ate it for dinner.

And that was the end of the pancake. And that is the end of the tale.

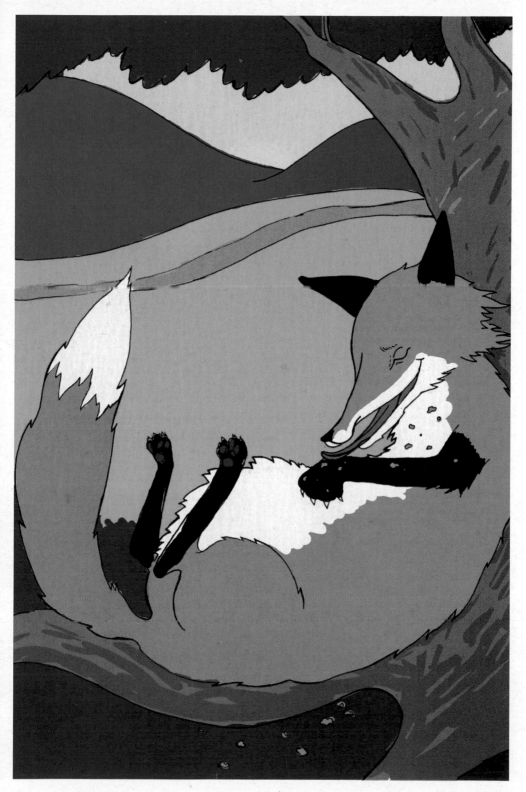

The Panther

Mike and Ann ran in.

"Dad," said Mike, "Please tell us a bedtime tale!"

"Yes," said Ann, clapping her hands. "Tell us a pancake tale."

"I would if I could," said their dad. "But I can't."

"Why not?" asked Mike.

"As far as I can tell, there is just one pancake ale."

"Oh no!" said Mike. "Now I'm in a sad mood."

"Let's sit down on Mike's bed," said their dad. I'll see if I can think of a good bedtime tale that ou will enjoy. Would you kids like a tale that has a anther in it?"

"What's a panfer?" Ann asked. Since she was just three, sometimes when she said /th/ it came out sounding like /f/.

"It's panther," said Mike with a smile.

"Panfer!" said Ann.

"Ug!" said Mike.

"Mike," said their dad. "Don't be mean. Be nice to your sister. She's just three. When you were her age, you made mistakes too."

"I did?"

Their dad nodded. Then he spoke to Ann. "A panther is a huge black cat that has sharp teeth."

"Tell it!" said Ann. "Tell the panfer tale!"

"OK," said their dad. "The name of this tale is *The Panther*."

Once there was a panther who could no longer hunt. His legs were just too tired. His joints were just too stiff. So he went in his cave and sat down near the mouth of the cave.

The panther still had to get food to eat. But how could he get food without hunting? At last he came up with a plan.

Soon, an owl came up to the mouth of the cave.

"How are you feeling, Panther?" the owl asked.

"Not so well," said the panther. "I am sick and can't leave my cave. Will you visit me in my cave? When someone is sick, it is so nice to have a pal visit." The owl went in for a visit. He stepped inside. But he did not step out.

Next a hare came hopping by.

"How are you feeling, Panther?" the hare asked.

"Not so well," said the panther. "I am sick. Will you visit me in my cave? When someone is sick, it is so nice to have a pal visit." The hare went inside the cave for a visit. He hopped inside. But he did not hop out.

Next a fox ran up.

"How are you feeling, Panther?" the fox asked.

"Not so well," said the panther. "I am sick. Will you visit me in my cave? When someone is sick, it is so nice to have a pal visit."

"Thanks," said the fox, "but no thanks!"

"Why not?" asked the panther.

"You can't fool me," said the fox. "I see lots of footprints going into your cave, but there are no footprints going out of it."

Moral: Be careful who you trust.

"What a clever fox," said Mike.

"I don't understand," shouted Ann. "What happened?"

"It seems that Mike is as smart as the fox," said the dad. "Perhaps he can tell you the reason the fox said 'No thanks!' to the panther."

"The fox is smart," Mike said. "He tricked the pancake and could tell that the panther was tricking him. You can't trick a trickster like the fox!"

Cat and Mouse Keep House

"Dad," said Mike, "can you tell us a bedtime tale that has a trick in it?"

"A trickster tale?" asked the dad.

"Yes!" shouted the kids with one voice.

"OK," said the dad. "The name of this tale is *Cat and Mouse Keep House*."

Once, a cat and a mouse set up house.

"We must get some food for the winter," said the mouse.

"Yes," said the cat. "We must indeed."

So the two of them went out and got a jar of jam.

"Where can we hide this jar of jam to keep it safe?" asked the cat.

"Let's hide it in the house next door," said the cat. "No one is in that house."

"Yes," said the mouse. "The old house next door is just the place!"

So the cat and the mouse hid the jar of jam in a dark corner of the house next door. They said that they would let it sit there until winter came.

A week passed. The cat felt a pang of hunger. He started thinking of the jar of jam. What if he went and had just a bit of jam for a snack? There would still be a lot left.

The cat made a plan to trick the mouse.

"Mouse," said the cat, "I must run off for a bit. Will you keep the house while I am out?"

The cat ran to the house next door and got out the jar. He started licking the jam. He licked and licked. When he stopped there was just a bit of jam left. Then he ran back home.

A week passed. This time it was the mouse who felt a pang of hunger.

"The cat is napping," he said to himself. "I think I will visit the house and get myself a snack. I will just have a bit of the jam. What's the harm in that? There will still be a lot left."

The mouse ran to the house next door. When he got there, what did he see? A jar with no jam! The cat had tricked him. The mouse was mad. He ran back and woke up the cat.

"You tricked me!" said the mouse.

"Did I?" said the cat.

"You ate the jam we said we would save for winter! You had it for a snack!" the mouse yelled.

"Yes!" said the cat. "I could have you for a snack!"

But the mouse was too mad to stop.

"You tricked me!" he shouted. "Now we have no jam! Now we. . . ."

But he did not have time to finish his sentence. The cat pounced on the mouse and made an end of him.

Moral: Be careful who you trust.

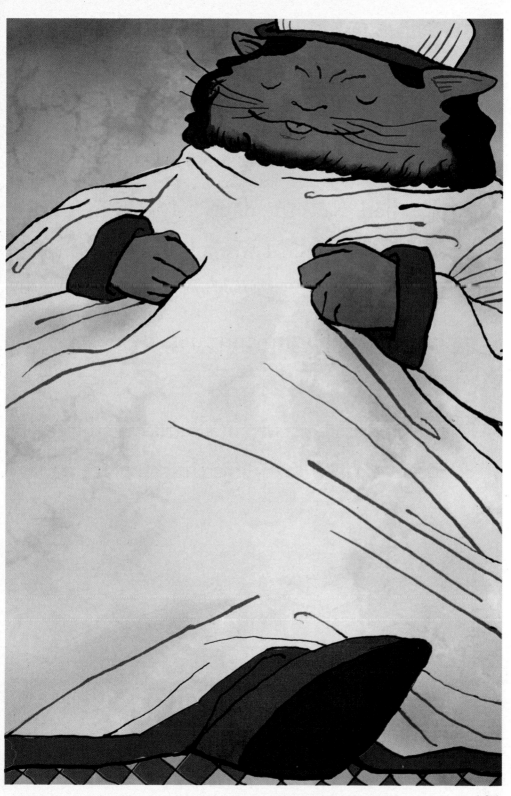

"What do you think is the point of the tale?" asked the dad. "Is there a point?"

Mike said, "I think that the point is that mice should not keep house with cats."

"I like that!" said the dad. "My dad used to tell me that tale when I was a kid. He said the point of it was: *Be careful who you trust.*"

Then the dad got up and tugged on the drapes.

"Look there!" he said. "It's dark outside. The street lamp is on. The tale is finished. It's time for bed."

About This Book

This book has been created for use by students learning to read with the Core Knowledge Language Arts Program. Readability levels are suitable for early readers. The book has also been carefully leveled in terms of its "code load," or the number of spellings used in the stories.

The English writing system is complex. It uses more than 200 spellings to stand for 40-odd sounds. Many sounds can be spelled several different ways, and many spellings can be pronounced several different ways. This book has been designed to make early reading experiences easier and more productive by using a subset of the available spellings. It uses *only* spellings that students have been taught to sound out as part of their phonics lessons, plus a handful of Tricky Words, which have also been deliberately introduced in the lessons. This means that the stories will be 100% decodable if they are assigned at the proper time.

As the students move through the program, they learn new spellings and the "code load" in the decodable readers increases gradually. The code load graphics on this page indicate the number of spellings students are expected to know in order to read the first story of the book and the number of spellings students are expected to know in order to read the final stories in the book. The columns on the inside back cover list the specific spellings and Tricky Words students are expected to recognize at the beginning of this Reader. The bullets at the bottom of the inside back cover identify spellings, Tricky Words, and other topics that are introduced gradually in the unit this Reader accompanies.

Visit us on the web at www.coreknowledge.org

CORE KNOWLEDGE LANGUAGE ARTS

SERIES EDITOR-IN-CHIEF
E. D. Hirsch, Jr.

PRESIDENT
Linda Bevilacqua

EDITORIAL STAFF
Carolyn Gosse, Senior Editor - Preschool
Sara Turnbull, Materials Development Manager
Michelle L. Warner, Senior Editor - Listening & Learning

Nick Anderson
Robin Blackshire
Maggie Buchanan
Paula Coyner
Sue Fulton
Sara Hunt
Erin Kist
Robin Luecke
Rosie McCormick
Cynthia Peng
Liz Pettit
Ellen Sadler
Deborah Samley
Diane Auger Smith
Sarah Zelinke

DESIGN AND GRAPHICS STAFF
Scott Ritchie, Creative Director

Kim Berrall
Michael Donegan
Liza Greene
Matt Leech
Bridget Moriarty
Lauren Pack

CONSULTING PROJECT MANAGEMENT SERVICES
ScribeConcepts.com

ADDITIONAL CONSULTING SERVICES
Ang Blanchette
Dorrit Green
Carolyn Pinkerton

ACKNOWLEDGMENTS

These materials are the result of the work, advice, and encouragement of numerous individuals over many years. Some of those singled out here already know the depth of our gratitude; others may be surprised to find themselves thanked publicly for help they gave quietly and generously for the sake of the enterprise alone. To helpers named and unnamed we are deeply grateful.

CONTRIBUTORS TO EARLIER VERSIONS OF THESE MATERIALS
Susan B. Albaugh, Kazuko Ashizawa, Nancy Braier, Kathryn M. Cummings, Michelle De Groot, Diana Espinal, Mary E. Forbes, Michael L. Ford, E. D. Hirsch, Danielle Knecht, James K. Lee, Diane Henry Leipzig, Martha G. Mack, Liana Mahoney, Isabel McLean, Steve Morrison, Juliane K. Munson, Elizabeth B. Rasmussen, Laura Tortorelli, Rachael L. Shaw, Sivan B. Sherman, Miriam E. Vidaver, Catherine S. Whittington, Jeannette A. Williams

We would like to extend special recognition to Program Directors Matthew Davis and Souzanne Wright who were instrumental to the early development of this program.

SCHOOLS
We are truly grateful to the teachers, students, and administrators of the following schools for their willingness to field test these materials and for their invaluable advice: Capitol View Elementary, Challenge Foundation Academy (IN), Community Academy Public Charter School, Lake Lure Classical Academy, Lepanto Elementary School, New Holland Core Knowledge Academy, Paramount School of Excellence, Pioneer Challenge Foundation Academy, New York City PS 26R (The Carteret School), PS 30X (Wilton School), PS 50X (Clara Barton School), PS 96Q, PS 102X (Joseph O. Loretan), PS 104Q (The Bays Water), PS 214K (Michael Friedsam), PS 223Q (Lyndon B. Johnson School), PS 308K (Clara Cardwell), PS 333Q (Goldie Maple Academy), Sequoyah Elementary School, South Shore Charter Public School, Spartanburg Charter School, Steed Elementary School, Thomas Jefferson Classical Academy, Three Oaks Elementary, West Manor Elementary.

And a special thanks to the CKLA Pilot Coordinators Anita Henderson, Yasmin Lugo-Hernandez, and Susan Smith, whose suggestions and day-to-day support to teachers using these materials in their classrooms was critical.

CREDITS

WRITERS
Matt Davis

ILUSTRATORS AND IMAGE SOURCES
Cover: Kathryn M. Cummings, Dustin Mackay, Steve Morrison; Title Page: Kathryn M. Cummings, Dustin Mackay, Steve Morrison; 1: Dustin Mackay; 2: Dustin Mackay; 3: Dustin Mackay; 4–5: Dustin Mackay; 6–7: Dustin Mackay; 8–9: Dustin Mackay; 10: Kathryn M. Cummings; 11: Kathryn M. Cummings; 12: Kathryn M. Cummings; 13: Kathryn M. Cummings; 14–15: Dustin Mackay; 16–17: Dustin Mackay; 19: Kathryn M. Cummings; 21: Kathryn M. Cummings; 22–23: Dustin Mackay; 24–25: Dustin Mackay; 27: Kathryn M. Cummings; 29: Kathryn M. Cummings; 31: Kathryn M. Cummings; 33: Kathryn M. Cummings; 34–35: Dustin Mackay; 37: Steve Morrison; 39: Steve Morrison; 41: Steve Morrison; 42–43: Dustin Mackay; 44–45: Dustin Mackay; 47: Steve Morrison; 48: Steve Morrison; 49: Steve Morrison; 50: Steve Morrison; 51: Steve Morrison; 52: Steve Morrison; 53: Steve Morrison; 54–55: Dustin Mackay; 57: Kathryn M. Cummings; 58: Kathryn M. Cummings; 59: Kathryn M. Cummings; 60: Kathryn M. Cummings; 61: Kathryn M. Cummings; 62–63: Dustin Mackay; 64–65: Dustin Mackay; 66: Kathryn M. Cummings; 67: Kathryn M. Cummings; 68: Kathryn M Cummings; 69: Kathryn M. Cummings; 71: Kathryn M. Cummings; 73: Kathryn M. Cummings; 75: Kathryn M. Cummings; 76–77: Dustin Mackay; 78–79: Dustin Mackay; 81: Kathryn M. Cummings; 83: Kathryn M. Cummings; 85: Kathryn M. Cummings; 86–87: Dustin Mackay; 88–89: Dustin Mackay; 91: Steve Morrison; 93: Steve Morrison; 94: Steve Morrison; 95: Steve Morrison; 97: Steve Morrison; 99: Steve Morrison; 100: Steve Morrison; 101: Steve Morrison; 102–103: Dustin Mackay